CW00376634

Improving
Comprehension

for ages 10-11

A & C Black • London

Contents

*Extract from 'Myths and Legends' by Anthony Horowitz. Reproduced by permission of United Agents and Anthony Horowitz

**Extract from 'Arthur, the Seeing Stone' by Kevin Crossley Holland. Reproduced by permission of Orion Books

***Extract from 'The Midnight Fox' by Betsy Byars. Reproduced by permission of Betsy Byars and Pollinger Ltd

****Extract from 'The Turbulent Term of Tyke Tyler' by Gene Kemp. Reproduced by permission of Gene Kemp and Pollinger Ltd.

Every effort has been made to trace copyright holders and to obtain their permission for use of copyright material. The publishers would be pleased to rectify any error in future editions.

Introduction

Improving Comprehension includes a range of interesting and exciting texts for sharing with pupils and using for reading comprehension. The texts have been carefully selected to be appropriate to the age group and to cover a range of text types. They reflect the demands of the Primary Framework for Literacy and in particular they following the learning objectives for Year 4. The accompanying comprehension worksheets are differentiated at three levels and are designed to be used by individuals or small groups. *Notes for teachers* are provided at the bottom of each worksheet providing guidance on how to get the most from the texts and how to approach the questions on the sheet.

For monitoring and recording purposes an *Individual record sheet* is provided on page 4 detailing reading and writing levels appropriate for Year 6. You may also find it helpful to refer to the *Contents* page where the 'texts' are linked to the relevant Assessment Focuses.

How to use the book and CD-ROM together

The book has fifteen 'texts', which can be projected on to a whiteboard for whole class use using the CD-ROM, or photocopied/printed for use with small groups or individuals. Sharing the text either on screen or on paper provides lots of opportunities for speaking and listening, for decoding words through a phonic approach, for reading and re-reading for meaning and for satisfaction and enjoyment in shared success.

For each text there are three comprehension worksheets at different ability levels to enable teachers to differentiate across the ability range. An animal picture at the top of the sheet indicates the level of the worksheet. The 'cat' exercises are at the simplest level; the 'dog' exercises are at the next level; the 'rabbit' exercises are at the most advanced level. You may decide to give some pupils the 'cat' worksheet and then decide, on the basis of their success, to ask them to complete the 'dog' worksheet. A similar approach could be taken with the 'dog' and 'rabbit' sheets.

After reading the text with the pupils the teacher should discuss the tasks with the children, ensuring that they understand clearly how to complete the worksheet and reminding them to answer the questions using full sentences and correct punctuation.

National Curriculum levels

The worksheets are aimed at the following ability levels:

  Cat worksheets are for pupils working at Level 3.
  Dog worksheets are for pupils working confidently at Level 4.
  Fish worksheets are for pupils who are working at Level 5.

Individual record sheet

Pupil's name: _____

Date of birth: _____

Reading Level 3

☐ I can read a range of texts fluently and accurately.
☐ I can read independently.
☐ I use strategies appropriately to establish meaning.
☐ In my responses to fiction I show understanding of the main points and I express preferences.

☐ In my responses to non-fiction I show understanding of the main points and I express preferences.
☐ I know the order of the alphabet.
☐ I use my knowledge of the alphabet to locate books and find information.

Reading Level 4

☐ I can respond to a range of texts.
☐ I show understanding of significant ideas, themes, events and characters.

☐ I am beginning to use inference and deduction.
☐ I refer to the text when explaining my views.
☐ I can locate and use ideas and information.

Reading Level 5

☐ I can understand a range of texts.
☐ I can select essential points and use inference and deduction where appropriate.
☐ In my responses, I can identify key features, themes and characters.

☐ I can select sentences, phrases and relevant information to support my views.
☐ I can retrieve and collate information from a range of sources.

Writing Level 3

☐ My writing is often organised, imaginative and clear.
☐ I use the main features of different forms of writing.
☐ I am beginning to adapt my writing to different readers.
☐ I use sequences of sentences to extend ideas logically.
☐ I choose words for variety and interest.

☐ The basic grammatical structure of my sentences is usually correct.
☐ My spelling is usually accurate, including that of common, polysyllabic words.
☐ I use punctuation accurately to mark sentences, including full stops, capital letters and question marks.
☐ My handwriting is joined and legible.

Writing Level 4

☐ I can write in a range of forms.
☐ My writing is lively and thoughtful.
☐ My ideas are often sustained and developed in interesting ways.
☐ My ideas are often organised appropriately for the purpose of the reader.
☐ My choice of vocabulary is often adventurous.
☐ I use words for effect.
☐ I am beginning to use grammatically complex sentences to extend meaning.

☐ My spelling, including that of polysyllabic words that conform to regular patterns, is generally accurate.
☐ I use full stops, capital letters and question marks are used correctly.
☐ I am beginning to use punctuation within the sentence.
☐ My handwriting is fluent, joined and legible.

Writing Level 5

☐ My writing is varied and interesting.
☐ I can convey meaning clearly in a range of forms for different readers.
☐ I can use a more formal style where appropriate.
☐ My vocabulary choices are imaginative.
☐ I can use words precisely.
☐ I organise simple and complex sentences into paragraphs.

☐ I usually spell words with complex regular patterns correctly.
☐ I can usually use accurately a range of punctuation, including commas, apostrophes and inverted commas.
☐ My handwriting is joined, clear and fluent.
☐ Where appropriate, I can adapt my handwriting to a range of tasks.

Daedalus and Icarus (Part 1)

Many stories, known as myths, were popular in the time of the Ancient Greeks. Myths were partly based on true events and on real people but, over time, the stories became altered or exaggerated. The Greek myth of Daedalus and Icarus is very well known.

Daedalus lived in the city of Athens and was descended from the first king of Athens. He was very skilful in designing buildings, in sculpture and in creating inventions but his career in Athens came to a sudden end when he committed a terrible crime. Daedulus had a nephew who worked for him as his apprentice but as the nephew became more skilled Daedulus grew jealous and was worried that the nephew was better than him. Daedalus threw his nephew to his death from a famous hill called the Acropolis.

For this awful murder Daedalus was sent away from Athens forever and he went to the island of Crete to work for King Minos. There he met a beautiful woman, Naucrate, and together they had a son who they named Icarus.

King Minos had a special job for Daedalus. He asked him to build a labyrinth prison, on a small island, for a dangerous monster called the Minotaur. Daedalus was a wonderful designer and he created an incredible labyrinth from which the Minotaur could not escape. People were thrown into the labyrinth to feed the Minotaur and they too were unable to find their way out. Daedalus, however, gave away the secret of the labyrinth to Ariadne, the daughter of King Minos. The king was very angry with Daedalus and threw both him and his son, Icarus, into the labyrinth.

Daedalus worked out a very clever way to escape from the labyrinth and the island. He had watched the sea birds flying overhead and he was convinced he could copy them. For months and months, he and Icarus collected as many feathers as they could. He built simple frames in the shape of wings and fastened the feathers to them with melted wax.

At last the wings were ready. Daedalus and Icarus were excited. Daedalus decided that his son would need some strong words of advice…

Andrew Brodie: Improving Comprehension for ages 10-11 © A&C Black Publishers Ltd 2008

Name: _____

Date: _____

Answer the questions, using full sentences.

1. What is this type of story called?

    _____

    _____

2. What did Daedalus do to his nephew?

    _____

    _____

3. To which island was Daedalus sent to live?

    _____

    _____

4. What special job did Daedalus do for King Minos?

    _____

    _____

5. How did King Minos punish Daedalus?

    _____

    _____

6. Who went with Daedalus when he was punished?

    _____

    _____

7. How did Daedalus plan to escape?

    _____

    _____

    _____

    _____

Notes for teachers
Year 6 pupils are likely to study Ancient Greece as part of the history curriculum and will probably learn some of the Greek myths. These myths are often complicated and difficult to grasp. Help the children to read the passage and ensure that they understand the story encouraging them to use a dictionary for any words they are not familiar with e.g. apprentice, labyrinth. The second part of this story is on page 9.

Daedalus and Icarus (Part 1)

Name: _____

Date: _____

Answer the questions using full sentences.

1. What talents did Daedalus have?

   _____

   _____

   _____

2. Why did Daedalus murder his nephew?

   _____

   _____

   _____

3. How was he punished for this crime?

   _____

   _____

4. Why was Daedalus punished again many years later?

   _____

   _____

   _____

5. How did Daedalus and Icarus prepare for their escape?

   _____

   _____

   _____

   _____

6. Daedalus gave Icarus some advice. What do you think the advice was? On a separate piece of paper write the conversation that they may have had.

Notes for teachers

Year 6 pupils are likely to study Ancient Greece as part of the history curriculum and will probably learn some of the Greek myths. They are often complicated and difficult to grasp. Some children might already know the story of Daedalus and Icarus and will know what to write for the final question. Others may have some good ideas of their own. The second part of this story is on page 9.

Andrew Brodie: Improving Comprehension for ages 10-11 © A&C Black Publishers Ltd 2008

Daedalus and Icarus (Part 1)

Name: _____

Date: _____

Answer the questions using full sentences.

1. In which city did Daedalus live and what famous hill in that city is mentioned in the story?

    _____

    _____

2. What three occupations did Daedalus have?

    _____

    _____

    _____

3. Why did Daedalus murder his nephew?

    _____

    _____

    _____

4. Why did King Minos throw Daedalus and Icarus into the labyrinth?

    _____

    _____

5. What do you think are the advantages and disadvantages of flight as their method of escape?

    _____

    _____

    _____

6. What type of monster is a Minotaur? Find the answer to this question by researching in the library or on the computer. Present your research findings on a separate piece of paper.

Notes for teachers
Year 6 pupils are likely to study Ancient Greece as part of the history curriculum and will probably learn some of the Greek myths. They are often very complicated and generally contain many long names. The children might need some help with question 5 e.g. the advantages of flight might include the fact that King Minor might not expect it and the disadvantages could include the fact that flying had never been tried before.

Andrew Brodie: Improving Comprehension for ages 10-11 © A&C Black Publishers Ltd 2008

Daedalus and Icarus (Part 2)

"You will need to take great care, Icarus. If you fly too near the surface of the sea the feathers will become waterlogged and fall off but don't fly too high either, because the sun will melt the wax."

"All right, all right," said Icarus, who didn't want to listen because he was so desperate to fly.

And with that, the two of them leapt into the air, flapped their wings and felt the power to fly. Up into the air they went, slowly at first but then more quickly as they grew more confident. The feeling of flying was amazing! Daedalus and Icarus soared and spiralled like the seabirds that Daedalus had observed so carefully. Icarus was especially good at flying and found that he could fly up quite high by flapping his wings quickly and strongly then he could simply glide back down, feeling the wind rushing through his hair.

Daedalus enjoyed watching his son flying so successfully using the wings that he had designed and created. He was impressed with his son's skill in flying and he was pleased with himself for even thinking of such an incredible idea. Every now and then he called to Icarus, "Well done, my son!" "Don't go too near the waves!" "Don't fly too near the sun!" And Icarus would call back, "I'm fine, I'm flying! I'm flying!"

Icarus flew faster and faster. He tried flying virtually straight up then swooping down again and found that he was able to achieve incredible speeds. The exhilaration of swooping down was worth all the effort of flapping his wings hard to reach the heights from which he could make the dive.

"Come on, Icarus. We must head for safety now," called Daedalus.

Icarus knew that the purpose of their flight was to escape from the island and to reach the mainland, but he decided that he would have one last swoop, one last amazing dive through the sky. "I'm coming, father. I'm just having one more go!" he called. He flapped his wings and rose higher up into the sky, then paused, ready to dive. But no, he could do better he thought ... so he rose another hundred metres ... then another hundred metres... He could hear his father's voice calling from below,

"Don't go too high. The sun will melt the wax."

A feather fell from his right wing. Then one fell from his left wing. Then another ... and another. Soon, feathers were falling quickly from both wings. Icarus watched the breeze catching the feathers, spinning them round and taking them out of his reach. He looked at the wax on his wings and was horrified to see the wax melting and the feathers coming unstuck. He began to drop through the sky. He found himself spinning and tumbling as more feathers were dislodged from the wax.

Daedalus watched in despair as he saw Icarus falling faster and faster. "No!" he called, but it was too late. Icarus plummeted from the sky straight into the sea.

Daedalus flew down, as low as he dared, but he saw no trace of his son except for the frames of the two wings floating on the surface. He searched and searched until it began to grow dark and then he turned to fly on alone, his salty tears falling into the salt water below him.

Andrew Brodie: Improving Comprehension for ages 10-11 © A&C Black Publishers Ltd 2008

Name: _____

Date: _____

Answer the questions using full sentences.

1. Why did Daedalus tell Icarus not to fly too near the sea?

    _____

    _____

2. Why did Daedalus tell Icarus not to fly too high?

    _____

    _____

3. Why did Icarus not want to listen?

    _____

    _____

4. Describe how Icarus felt about flying.

    _____

    _____

    _____

    _____

5. What happened when Icarus made his last flight?

    _____

    _____

    _____

    _____

6. How do you think Daedalus felt in the end?

    _____

    _____

    _____

    _____

Notes for teachers

Remind pupils of the first part of the story on page 5. Help the children to read this passage and ensure that they understand the story and that they can read any unfamiliar words. To answer the fourth and fifth questions the pupils will need to read parts of the story several times.

10

Daedalus and Icarus (Part 2)

Name: _____

Date: _____

Answer the questions, using full sentences.

1. What two pieces of advice did Daedalus give to Icarus?

   _____

   _____

2. How did Icarus react to the advice?

   _____

   _____

3. How did Daedalus feel when he was watching Icarus fly?

   _____

   _____

4. Why did Daedalus tell Icarus to 'come on'?

   _____

   _____

5. Why didn't Icarus come straight away?

   _____

   _____

   _____

6. Imagine that you are Icarus. Write a description of your last flight.

   _____

   _____

   _____

   _____

   _____

   _____

   _____

   _____

   _____

Notes for teachers
Do the pupils remember the first part of the Daedalus and Icarus story on page 5? Help the children to read this passage and ensure that they understand the story. Encourage the pupils to think carefully about the last task. Encourage them to write a detailed description of the last flight, from start to finish. They may need extra paper to complete the task.

Daedalus and Icarus (Part 2)

Name: _____

Date: _____

Answer the questions, using full sentences.

1. How did Daedalus know what advice to give Icarus?

   _____

   _____

2. It is unusual to start a sentence with the word 'and'. Why do you think that the writer has done this in two places?

   _____

   _____

3. At least four words beginning with the letter 's' are used in the story to describe the process of flying. List these words.

   _____   _____

   _____   _____

4. Imagine that you can fly. Write a sentence to describe flying that uses as many 's' words as possible.

   _____

   _____

   _____

5. Describe a time when you have been asked to stop doing something but you continued anyway! Were there any consequences?

   _____

   _____

   _____

   _____

6. Imagine that you are Daedalus. On a separate piece of paper write a description of watching the last flight that Icarus made.

Notes for teachers
Do the pupils remember the first part of the Daedalus and Icarus story on page 5? Help the children to read this passage and ensure that they understand the story. The second question is designed to encourage the pupils to look at the text again and to read and reread the appropriate sentences, together with the sentences that come before them – encourage them to express their own ideas as to why the sentences start with 'and'.

Andrew Brodie: Improving Comprehension for ages 10-11 © A&C Black Publishers Ltd 2008

The Eye of the Cyclops

This extract is from a Greek myth, retold by the author Anthony Horowitz in his book 'The Eye of the Cyclops'.

 The Cyclops was certainly a terrifying creature. It was about the height of a two-storey house with thick, curly hair, a matted (and usually filthy) beard and only one eye set square in the middle of its forehead. It was grotesquely ugly, extremely bad-tempered, inordinately violent and generally worth going a long way to avoid. All this, any good book of Greek myths will tell you. But what is less often mentioned is the fact that the Cyclops was also incredibly stupid. It was probably one of the most stupid monsters that ever lived.

 There were a great many Cyclopes. At one time they had been employed as blacksmiths for Zeus but after a while they had forgotten not only how to do the work but what the work was that they were supposed to do, and had become shepherds instead. They were shepherds for almost two hundred years before it occurred to them to go and buy some sheep. Then they took their sheep and settled on an island in the middle of the Aegean Sea where they lived in caves, seldom if ever talking to one another. There were two reasons for this. The first was that the Cyclopes were poor conversationalists, often forgetting the beginning of a sentence when they were only half-way through. But also, if there was one thing a Cyclops couldn't stand, it was another Cyclops.

 The most famous Cyclops was called Polyphemus. He was the son of Poseidon, the god of the sea, but preferred to stay very much on land, looking after a flock of sheep. Polyphemus had no friends but was on intimate terms with most of the sheep. He knew them all by name, milked them as gently as his huge fingers could manage and shed real tears whenever he had to slaughter one in order to make his particularly delicious lamb stew.

 One day returning to his cave after a hard day's work in the hills, he was astonished to find that he had had visitors. They were still there in fact, sitting in front of his fire and feasting on one of his sheep. There were about a dozen of them and looking more closely he was delighted to see that they were human beings.

 Polyphemus loved human beings in his own way …which was cooked or raw. What he particularly liked about them was the way their bones crunched between his teeth but never got caught in his throat.

 The giant's face lit up in a great smile. It was also a horrible smile for, having just one eye in the middle of his forehead, everything he did with his face was rather horrible.

Andrew Brodie: Improving Comprehension for ages 10-11 © A&C Black Publishers Ltd 2008

The Eye of the Cyclops

Name: _____

Date: _____

Ring the correct answer for each of the following three questions.

1. What type of story is 'The Eye of the Cyclops'?

   fairy tale   legend   myth   biography

2. What was the most famous Cyclops called?

   Polyphemus   Poseidon   Zeus   Horowitz

3. In what did the Cyclops live?

   houses   islands   caves   the sea

The following two questions should each be answered with a simple sentence. The first one has been started for you.

4. Who was Poseidon?

   Poseidon was the god of _____

5. Would the Cyclops be described as incredibly clever or incredibly stupid?

   _____

   _____

6. Read the text and use the clues to help you imagine what a Cyclops looks like. Draw a Cyclops in the box.

Andrew Brodie: Improving Comprehension for ages 10-11 © A&C Black Publishers Ltd 2008

The Eye of the Cyclops

Name: _____

Date: _____

Ring the correct answer for each of the following questions.

1.   How many visitors did Polyphemus have?

   three   twelve   twenty   thirty

2.   What is the plural of the word Cyclops?

   Cyclopses   Cyclopes   Cycloponess   Cycles

Answer each of the following questions with a sentence.

3.   Why would you try to avoid a Cyclops?

   _____

   _____

4.   Where did the Cyclopes settle with their sheep?

   _____

   _____

5.   How did Polyphemus like to eat human beings?

   _____

   _____

6.   What job did the Cyclopes once do for Zeus?

   _____

   _____

   _____

7.   On a separate piece of paper draw and label a picture of Polyphemus looking after his sheep in the hills.

Notes for teachers

Ensure the children have read and understood the passage, paying particular attention to any unfamiliar vocabulary. Four of the questions on this page ask pupils to use complete sentences; these should be correctly spelled and punctuated. For the final task, the picture should show how big the Cyclops is next to the normal sized sheep, as well as showing the main features of the Cyclops, e.g. beard, hair, single eye, etc.

Andrew Brodie: Improving Comprehension for ages 10-11 © A&C Black Publishers Ltd 2008

The Eye of the Cyclops

Name: _____

Date: _____

1. Ring the word below that is nearest in meaning to the word 'inordinately'.

   extremely   angrily   cheerfully   often

2. Ring the word below that is nearest in meaning to the word 'slaughter'.

   cook   hurt   kill   entertain

Answer each of the following questions with well-written detailed sentences.

3. As shepherds, what was the first mistake the Cyclopes made and how long was it before they realised their error?

   _____

   _____

4. Why was Polyphemus delighted to be visited by humans even though they were feasting on one of his sheep?

   _____

   _____

5. Where was the Island on which Polyphemus lived?

   _____

   _____

6. What made Polyphemus cry?

   _____

   _____

7. Give two reasons why the Cyclopes rarely talked to one another.

   _____

   _____

   _____

   _____

   _____

Andrew Brodie: Improving Comprehension for ages 10-11 © A&C Black Publishers Ltd 2008

Conkers

The following extract concerns a boy called Robbie who is bullied by two other boys, Wayne and Shayne.

The twins shouted swearwords at Robbie the whole way. He walked faster, they walked faster. He started to jog, they started to jog. He started to run, they started to run.

Robbie contemplated taking the short cut that connected Greenway Lane to Oldroad Park but he decided that would be silly as the path was so narrow and secluded that if they caught him they would be able to do anything to him. So, although he was getting exhausted, Robbie carried on running up the slope of Greenway Lane. Then he reached the three conker trees.

The twins stopped as they couldn't resist picking up conkers. Robbie glanced back, then slowed down a bit, as he was really out of breath. He looked back. Yes, they were busy, so Robbie slowed to a walk.

Minutes later, Robbie sighed with relief as he turned into Oldroad Park. 'Safe,' he thought to himself as he could see his house about two hundred metres ahead.

Suddenly Robbie felt his back being pelted with something very hard and spiky. Wayne and Shayne were just behind him with armfuls of conkers still in their shells. They had obviously doubled back and cut through the pathway to reach Oldroad Park at about the same time as Robbie.

Showers of sharp conker shells rained down on Robbie. He simply curled into a ball with his arms protecting his head. The conkers continued to come pounding down on his head and body. The two boys were picking up the fallen ammunition and firing it again and again. They were shrieking with enjoyment over the success of their attack but suddenly their shrieks turned to yelps of pain.

Cautiously Robbie looked up and, with amazement, he saw Wayne and Shayne themselves doubled up in defensive positions.

There was Erica, dressed in her tennis outfit, wielding her tennis racket, picking up conkers with astonishing speed and belting them as hard as she could at Robbie's attackers.

"Don't you dare touch my brother again!" she shouted, with a ferocity that Robbie had only ever seen reserved for him.

Andrew Brodie: Improving Comprehension for ages 10-11 © A&C Black Publishers Ltd 2008

Conkers

Name: _____

Date: _____

Answer the questions, using *full* sentences. Check your punctuation carefully.

1. How do we know that Wayne and Shayne are brothers?

   _____

   _____

   _____

2. Which roads did Robbie go along?

   _____

   _____

3. How many conker trees were there?

   _____

   _____

4. Why did Robbie think that he was safe?

   _____

   _____

   _____

   _____

5. Who rescued Robbie? Can you explain why?

   _____

   _____

   _____

   _____

6. Robbie was very scared. On a separate piece of paper describe a time when you were scared.

18

Conkers

Answer the questions, using full sentences.

1. How did Robbie try to get away from the twins at first?

    _____

    _____

2. Why did Robbie decide not to take the short cut?

    _____

    _____

3. Why did Wayne and Shayne stop?

    _____

    _____

4. What is the real name for a conker tree? You may need to use the internet or a library to find the answer.

    _____

    _____

5. Why did the twins stop attacking Robbie?

    _____

    _____

6. You may have been bullied or you may have a friend who has. Write about what it is like and how it might make you feel?

    _____

    _____

    _____

    _____

    _____

    _____

Notes for teachers

Help the children to read the passage and talk about how Robbie was feeling. Did he do the right thing? The last task will need to be handled sensitively so that pupils don't get upset or, conversely, that they don't see any glory in the idea of bullying. You could extend this activity by asking pupils to design a leaflet on how to prevent bullying in school.

Conkers

Name: _____

Date: _____

Answer the questions, using full sentences.

1. Why did Robbie run faster and what effect do you think this had on the twins?

   _____

   _____

   _____

2. Robbie chose not to take the short cut but what problems did this cause?

   _____

   _____

   _____

3. Why did Robbie slow down?

   _____

   _____

4. Robbie curled into a ball. What would you have done?

   _____

   _____

   _____

5. How did Erica rescue Robbie?

   _____

   _____

6. Do you think Erica was older or younger than Robbie?

   _____

   _____

7. Robbie was on his way home from school. On a separate piece of paper continue the story and describe what happened when Robbie went to school the next day.

Notes for teachers

Help the children to read this passage and discuss the main events of the story. Did Robbie do the right thing? What do the children think he should have done? The last task will need discussion and pupils may like to talk through their ideas before putting anything down on paper.

Charles Dickens

The text below is a brief biography of the author Charles Dickens. In the frame around the edge of the text you will find the titles of some of his stories – perhaps you may have heard of some of them.

The famous English author Charles Dickens was born in the south of England in February 1812, moving to London in 1814. Although his family was not wealthy Charles was lucky enough to be sent to school at the age of nine, in an age when education was an expensive privilege. Just three years later he had to find work, as his father was imprisoned for debt and unable to pay for his schooling. Fortunately after just six months, his father inherited enough money to pay off his debts and was released from prison. He could afford to pay for Charles to be educated again.

When Charles Dickens left school at fifteen he was employed by a firm of solicitors as an office clerk but he really wanted to be a journalist and so, with this in mind, he taught himself shorthand. He became very skilled at shorthand and soon learned to transcribe speeches accurately and quickly. He was then able to find work as a reporter and he worked for a number of papers.

Charles Dickens' first piece of published work was a short story, written under the pseudonym 'Boz', that appeared in a magazine in 1833. Several more short stories followed this. His first novel, The Pickwick Papers, was originally published in monthly instalments at a cost of one shilling per instalment, with the first episode of this being available in 1836.

Dickens was soon a very successful novelist but continued to work for a range of magazines and papers. Amongst his most famous stories are A Christmas Carol, Oliver Twist and A Tale of Two Cities, all of which have been made into films and are still enjoyed today.

This prolific author died in 1870. By then he had become a famous and important person and so was buried in Westminster Abbey, London.

THE HAUNTED MAN

GREAT EXPECTATIONS

Bleak House

Oliver Twist

Nicholas Nickleby

THE OLD CURIOSITY SHOP

The Pickwick Papers   David Copperfield

21

Charles Dickens

Ring the correct answer for each of the following three questions.

1. The year in which Charles Dickens was born was

    1218   1818   1212   1812

2. What career did the young Charles Dickens hope for?

    office boy   prison officer   typist   journalist

3. What was Charles Dickens very good at?

    shorthand   shining   talking   shopping

The following questions should be answered with a simple sentence. The first one has been started for you.

4. Where is Charles Dickens buried?

    Charles Dickens is buried in _____

5. What was the first job Charles Dickens had?

    _____

    _____

6. What was the title of Dickens' first novel?

    _____

    _____

7. In which year did Dickens die?

    _____

    _____

Notes for teachers

Read the passage with the children and discuss the main features of Charles Dickens' life. Are they familiar with any of his novels (listed around the passage) or have they seen any films based on his books? Do they know what shorthand is and have they ever seen it written down? Encourage the children to compose their sentences out loud before writing anything down.

Andrew Brodie: Improving Comprehension for ages 10-11 © A&C Black Publishers Ltd 2008

Charles Dickens

Name: _____

Date: _____

Ring the correct answer for each of the following two questions.

1. Which of the definitions below best describes the word 'pseudonym'?

    a different name   a silly name   a long name   a set of initials

2. Which of the definitions below is nearest in meaning to 'journalist'?

    story writer   reporter   entertainer   solicitor

Answer each of the following questions with a full sentence.

3. What job did Charles Dickens want?

    _____

    _____

4. What was the name of his first novel?

    _____

    _____

5. How old was Charles Dickens when he died? Explain how you know this.

    _____

    _____

    _____

    _____

6. On the text page, a number of Charles Dickens' story titles appear. Sort them into alphabetical order and list them below.

    _____   _____

    _____   _____

    _____   _____

    _____   _____

Notes for teachers
Ensure the children have read and understood the passage, paying particular attention to any unfamiliar vocabulary. Discuss the significant parts of Dickens' life. The final task is designed not only to make pupils take note of the titles featured in the text and around its border but also to encourage them to consider how best to sort them, i.e. by the first or last word of the title. They should see that there is more than one way that could be correct.

23

Charles Dickens

Answer each of the following questions with well-written detailed sentences.

1. Charles' father was imprisoned for debt. Explain in your own words the meaning of 'debt'.

    _____

    _____

2. How was Charles' later education paid for?

    _____

    _____

3. Would you have been able to buy the final instalment of 'The Pickwick Papers' in 1836? Explain your answer.

    _____

    _____

4. Charles Dickens was very good at shorthand. Explain what this is and how it helped him. You might need to look this up in a book or on the internet.

    _____

    _____

5. How are Charles Dickens' stories still enjoyed today even by those who have not read them?

    _____

    _____

    _____

    _____

6. One of Dickens' stories was set in Paris and London. Explain how you know which story this is.

    _____

    _____

Notes for teachers

The second question should demonstrate that the pupils have realised that the book was not completed in 1836. The author has simply said that the first episode was available in that year. When answering the third question pupils should find out that shorthand is a system of symbols that represent words so that people can quickly write things down word for word. This is a good group discussion point.

Andrew Brodie: Improving Comprehension for ages 10-11 © A&C Black Publishers Ltd 2008

A Christmas Carol

The following extract is from 'A Christmas Carol' by Charles Dickens. In this story the central character is visited by a series of three ghosts in his bedroom on Christmas Eve. These visitations, representing his past life, his present life and a likely future, resulted in him becoming a much more generous person with a happier future. In the extract, Scrooge is just finishing work on Christmas Eve and going home for the night.

At length the hour of shutting up the counting house arrived. With an ill-will Scrooge dismounted from his stool, and tacitly admitted the fact to the expectant clerk in the Tank, who instantly snuffed his candle out, and put on his hat.

"You'll want all day to-morrow, I suppose?" said Scrooge.

"If quite convenient sir."

"It's not convenient," said Scrooge, "and it's not fair. If I was to stop half-a-crown for it, you'd think yourself ill-used, I'll be bound?"

The clerk smiled faintly.

"And yet," said Scrooge, "you don't think me ill-used, when I pay a day's wages for no work."

The clerk observed that it was only once a year.

"A poor excuse for picking a man's pocket every twenty-fifth of December!" said Scrooge, buttoning his great-coat up to the chin. "But I suppose you must have the whole day. Be here all the earlier next morning."

The clerk promised he would; and Scrooge walked out with a growl. The office was closed in a twinkling, and the clerk, with the long ends of his white comforter dangling below his waist (for he boasted no great-coat), went down a slide on Cornhill, at the end of a lane of boys, twenty times, in honour of its being Christmas Eve, and then ran home to Camden Town as hard as he could pelt, to play at blind man's-buff.

Scrooge took his melancholy dinner in his usual melancholy tavern; and having read all his newspapers, and beguiled the rest of the evening with his banker's-book, went home to bed. He lived in chambers, which had once belonged to his deceased partner. They were a gloomy suite of rooms, in a lowering pile of building up a yard, where it had so little business to be, that one could scarcely help fancying it must have run there when it was a young house, playing at hide-and-seek with other houses, and forgotten the way out again. It was old enough now, and dreary enough, for nobody lived in it but Scrooge, the other rooms being all let as offices. The yard was so dark that even Scrooge, who knew its every stone, was fain to grope with his hands. The fog and frost so hung about the black gateway of the house, that it seemed as if the Genius of the Weather sat in mournful meditation on the threshold.

Andrew Brodie: Improving Comprehension for ages 10-11 © A&C Black Publishers Ltd 2008

A Christmas Carol

Name: _____

Date: _____

Ring the correct answer for each of the following three questions.

1.   How many ghosts visited Scrooge?

   two   three   four   five

2.   Which day of the year is featured it in the extract?

   December 23rd   December 24th   December 25th   December 26th

3.   How often did the clerk ask for a paid day off?

   once a month   once a week   once a fortnight   once a year

**The following questions should each be answered with a simple sentence.
The first one has been started for you.**

4.   Who is the central character in the story?

   The central character is _____

5.   What did the clark do in Corn Hall?

   _____

   _____

6.   Where did Scrooge eat his dinner?

   _____

   _____

7.   Who is the author of this story?

   _____

   _____

Andrew Brodie: Improving Comprehension for ages 10-11 © A&C Black Publishers Ltd 2008

A Christmas Carol

Name: _____

Date: _____

Ring the correct answer for each of the following two questions.

1. How much money is the clerk paid for a day's work?

    one pound   five pence   half a crown

2. Which of the words below is nearest in meaning to 'comforter'?

    a packet of sweets   a woolly scarf   a type of coat   a pair of gloves

Answer each of the following questions with a full sentence.

3. In 'A Christmas Carol', how many ghosts visited Scrooge?

    _____

    _____

4. Which two words are used to describe the weather in the extract?

    _____

    _____

5. What did Scrooge read while he was in the tavern having dinner?

    _____

    _____

6. What did he do for the rest of the evening?

    _____

    _____

7. How long a holiday was the clerk given for Christmas? How you know this?

    _____

    _____

    _____

Notes for teachers
Ensure the children have read and understood the passage, paying particular attention to any unfamiliar vocabulary. Pupils should understand that as it was written so long ago there are more unfamiliar words and phrases than in a more modern text. Most of the questions on this page ask pupils to use complete sentences; these should be correctly spelled and punctuated. When answering the question about what Scrooge read, pupils should include both newspapers and his 'banker's book'.

Andrew Brodie: Improving Comprehension for ages 10-11 © A&C Black Publishers Ltd 2008

A Christmas Carol

Name: _____

Date: _____

1. Ring the word nearest in meaning to 'melancholy'

   cheerful   tasty   lonely   gloomy

2. Ring the word nearest in meaning to 'counting house'.

   accountant   factory   restaurant   cinema

3. Ring the word nearest in meaning to 'twinkling' as it is used in the text.

   shiny   happy   moment   smile

4. What time of day is it at the beginning of the extract? Use the text to explain your answer.

   _____

   _____

   _____

5. Explain the meaning of the phrase, 'for he boasted no great coat'.

   _____

   _____

   _____

6. In your own words, describe where Scrooge lived.

   _____

   _____

   _____

   _____

   _____

Notes for teachers

Discuss the extract with the children, and analyse words and phrases they may not be familiar with. The final question is particularly thought provoking as pupils need to understand the term 'chambers', as well as being able to describe the building where the rooms are and also what the other rooms in the building are used for.

Andrew Brodie: Improving Comprehension for ages 10-11 © A&C Black Publishers Ltd 2008

The reality is rarely as good as the dream

At ten years old Paige knew exactly what she wanted in life – fame and fortune. She had been dreaming of this for as long as she could remember. What could be better, she asked herself, than a celebrity lifestyle? It seemed that to achieve this ambition she didn't have to be very good at anything! She would be asked to appear on T.V., be invited to 'red carpet' film premieres, meet pop stars and famous actors and be paid vast amounts of money to do these things. Whilst Paige wasn't too sure how to achieve her ambition she was sure that she would manage it somehow.

On this particular evening however, her future dreams had to be put to one side whilst she did her homework. At school they had been reading 'A Christmas Carol' by Charles Dickens, a story in which the central character, Scrooge, was visited by a series of ghosts who showed him his life and what it could be like. Her task this evening was to write a story based on this famous tale. Paige was bored and couldn't think of anything to write. After all, celebrities did not need to write stories based on those of famous authors. She was listening to music and yawning as she looked at the blank sheet of paper that stared back at her accusingly.

As she stared at the paper the world seemed to fade away and the empty sheet took on a life of its own. There was a title at the top, 'The reality is rarely as good as the dream'. 'How did that get there?' thought Paige, 'I didn't write it.' Pictures began to appear on the paper, moving scenes starring Paige herself. Staring at them intently, she wondered what would happen next.

In the first scene, Paige saw herself arriving at school and everyone seemed to be her friend. They were all asking her what it was like to be on T.V., and whether they could go shopping with her at the weekend. Paige was quite a popular girl, but in this she saw herself surrounded by classmates who wouldn't normally spend time with her. After watching for a while she realised that the Paige in the book was rather uncomfortable, wondering which of her classmates were really her friends and which of them just wanted to be seen with a celebrity.

The paper slowly cleared and another scene began to appear. In this scene she saw a group of her classmates talking about a forthcoming birthday party that one of them was having. They were wondering just what sort of present she would be taking to the party. Fran, a girl who she hadn't known long, said, 'I bet Paige will show off by turning up with a present that is more expensive than any of us could afford.' Another replied that if she only took an ordinary gift it would be mean, as she had more money than any of the others. Paige began to think that this celebrity lifestyle she yearned for might not be as easy as she thought.

As she was considering this, another picture began to move on to the paper. In this she saw herself as she really was, with her good friends that she liked and trusted. She was not dreaming of a different life but enjoying the one she had and making the most of all the opportunities that school offered her. As this final picture faded leaving only the writing at the top of the paper, Paige, began to understand the title that was there and realised she had a good idea for a story too. She yawned, stretched, and began to write.

Andrew Brodie: Improving Comprehension for ages 10-11 © A&C Black Publishers Ltd 2008

The reality is rarely as good as the dream

Name: _____

Date: _____

Ring the correct answer for each of the following three questions.

1. The girl in the story is called

    Page   Peggy   Paige   Paisley

2. Which of the words below is used to describe the lifestyle she wanted

    celebrity   wealthy   happy   hard working

3. Which book had she been reading at school?

    Great Expectations   A Christmas Carol

    The Pickwick Papers   A Tale of Two Cities

Each of the following questions should be answered with a simple sentence. The first one has been started for you.

4. How old was the main character in the story?

    The main character in the story was _____

5. What book had Paige been reading at school?

    _____

    _____

6. What did Paige have to do for her homework?

    _____

    _____

7. What is the title of the story?

    _____

    _____

Notes for teachers

Make sure the children have read and understood the passage, paying particular attention to any unfamiliar vocabulary. Can they see the connection between this and 'A Christmas Carol'? Encourage the children to compose their answers out loud before writing anything down.

Andrew Brodie: Improving Comprehension for ages 10-11 © A&C Black Publishers Ltd 2008

The reality is rarely as good as the dream

Name: _____

Date: _____

1. Ring the word below that correctly describes the text.

   biography   factual   reference   fiction

2. Write a definition for the word 'ambition'.

   ambition _____

   _____

Answer each of the following questions with a sentence.

3. Explain why, in paragraph two, Paige was bored.

   _____

   _____

   _____

4. What was it about a celebrity lifestyle that Paige thought she would enjoy?

   _____

   _____

   _____

5. Write the sentence from paragraph three that tells the reader that Paige is falling asleep and beginning to dream.

   _____

   _____

   _____

6. Write the sentence in paragraph four that tells us that Paige is well liked.

   _____

   _____

   _____

Notes for teachers
Discuss the passage with the children and see whether they have noticed the similarities between this and 'A Christmas Carol'. When writing a definition for 'ambition' pupils should not use a dictionary – you may however want them to refer to a dictionary later when discussing their answers. The correct answer to the third question should include both reasons for Paige being bored, i.e. that she had to do her homework rather than dreaming of fame of fortune, and that she couldn't think of anything to write.

The reality is rarely as good as the dream

Name: _____

Date: _____

Answer each of the following questions with a well-written detailed sentence.

1. Paige thought that to be a celebrity you didn't have to be very good at anything. Do you agree with this? Give reasons for your answer.

    _____

    _____

    _____

2. How many different scenes did Paige see in her dream?

    _____

    _____

3. How does the reader know that Paige is a frequent daydreamer? Use the text to explain your answer.

    _____

    _____

    _____

4. In your own words give two reasons, referred to in the text, why being a young celebrity might be very difficult.

    _____

    _____

    _____

    _____

5. Explain the title ' The reality is rarely as good as the dream'

    _____

    _____

    _____

    _____

Notes for teachers

Make sure the children have read and understood the passage and discuss the way the author has combined reality and dreams. The first question asks for an opinion to be expressed so any well reasoned and written answer can be accepted.

Andrew Brodie: Improving Comprehension for ages 10-11 © A&C Black Publishers Ltd 2008

Victorian times

The following extract concerns a young boy called Robbie who has managed to travel back in time to the year 1875, although he does not realise this yet. He has met a girl called Charlotte who is showing him round the garden of her rather grand home. Robbie has visited the house and the gardens on another occasion.

They walked on slowly, along a tidy gravel driveway, until Robbie heard the rumble of wheels and the sound of hooves as a horse-drawn carriage charged up behind them. They had to step off the driveway on to the lawn to avoid being run over.

"Wow!" said Robbie. "That's impressive. Where are the cameras?"

"What cameras?" asked Charlotte, then continued, "My mother has a friend called Mrs Cameron. She has a camera. Mother thinks it is very strange for a woman to have a new invention like that. But Mrs Cameron is coming to make a picture of me soon. She makes a portrait without using paints. Do you know how a camera works? It's very clever."

"No, I don't actually," replied Robbie, thinking briefly of his own digital camera at home. But his thoughts didn't linger on this; instead his mind was whirring like a dozen computers. He had stubbornly held on to the idea that this was a film set but the evidence was building up against this.

Suddenly his doubts became even stronger. They had reached the old stables. He recognised the outside of them from the last time he came here with Mum and Erica and they had had a cream tea. But as soon as he and Charlotte passed through the gateway everything was so different.

There were no big glass doors; instead there were big wooden doors swung open to reveal three shining carriages. There were no wooden picnic tables; where they had been when Robbie had last visited, the carriage that had driven past them was now standing and luggage was being lifted from it. There was no gift shop; there were tack rooms with leather reins and saddles and shining brasses. There were no public toilets; there were stables, with rows of horses' heads showing above the half-doors. Four horses were being rubbed down in the yard by four men wearing leather aprons. These were obviously the horses that had just pulled the carriage up the long gravel drive.

Robbie looked around very carefully: at the ground, at the walls and up to the roofs. There were no cameras to be seen anywhere. "What year is this?" he asked Charlotte.

"Robert Vincent Smith, do you not know anything?" she responded.

"What year is this?" he asked, unable to conceal the desperation in his voice.

"Eighteen seventy-five, of course," replied Charlotte.

Andrew Brodie: Improving Comprehension for ages 10-11 © A&C Black Publishers Ltd 2008

Name: _____

Date: _____

Answer the questions, using full sentences with correct punctuation.

1. What did Robbie find impressive?

    _____

    _____

    _____

2. Two people in the passage have cameras. Who are they?

    _____

    _____

    _____

3. How many carriages were at the stables? Explain how you know.

    _____

    _____

    _____

    _____

4. Robbie expected to see wooden picnic tables. What else did he expect to see?

    _____

    _____

    _____

5. Why were the horses being rubbed down?

    _____

    _____

6. Imagine that you could travel to another time. What time would you travel to
    and why? Write your answer on a separate piece of paper.

Notes for teachers
Help the children to read this passage and ensure that they understand the story. Some children may have
difficulty with the concept of Robbie visiting a place, over a hundred years ago, that he had visited before in
modern times. It may be helpful if you can think of a local stately home to discuss with the pupils.

Name: _____

Date: _____

Answer the questions, using full sentences.

1. Describe the way the carriage came up the drive.

   _____

   _____

   _____

2. What does Charlotte consider to be a 'new invention'?

   _____

   _____

   _____

3. What did Robbie have to eat when he last visited the stables and why could he not have the same this time?

   _____

   _____

   _____

4. Who was Robbie with when he last visited the stables?

   _____

   _____

   _____

5. Why did Robbie look round very carefully?

   _____

   _____

   _____

6. Imagine that you could travel back ten years and see yourself and your own home. Describe what you might find, giving as much detail as possible. Write your answer on a separate piece of paper.

Notes for teachers
Help the children to read this passage and ensure that they understand the story – some children may have difficulty with the concept of Robbie visiting a place, over a hundred years ago, that he has visited before in modern times.

Andrew Brodie: Improving Comprehension for ages 10-11 © A&C Black Publishers Ltd 2008

Victorian times

Name: _____

Date: _____

Answer the questions, using full sentences.

1. Why would it be strange for a woman to have a new invention in 1875?

    _____

    _____

2. Mrs Cameron was a real person. Research her name on the internet. What was her full name?

    _____

    _____

3. Why did Robbie think that he was on the set of a film?

    _____

    _____

    _____

4. Why did Robbie begin to doubt that it was a film set?

    _____

    _____

    _____

5. Describe the stables as Robbie finds them on his visit with Charlotte.

    _____

    _____

    _____

    _____

6. Imagine that you could travel forward ten years and see yourself and your own home. On a separate piece of paper describe what you might find, giving as much detail as possible.

Notes for teachers
Help the children to read this passage and ensure that they understand the story – some children may have difficulty with the concept of Robbie visiting a place, over a hundred years ago, that he has visited before in modern times. It may be helpful if you can think of a local stately home to discuss with the pupils.

Broken ice

The following extract is from the book 'Arthur, the Seeing Stone' by Kevin Crossley-Holland. This passage concerns Arthur, aged 13, his friend Gatty, aged 12, and Arthur's younger sister Sian.

This was when I heard a loud crack, and then a scream from the fish-pond.

'Sian,' I yelled, and I raced round the hedge and over to the pond. Sian had gone through the ice, at least ten steps out. She was in the water up to her shoulders, clutching on to the jagged edge of the ice-sheet with her white fingers.

'Arthur!' she screamed.

'Keep still!' I shouted. 'Don't try to move.'

'Help!' screamed Sian.

'I'm coming,' I called.

At the edge of the pond, I lay down on the ice and began to pull and slide my way across. I looked down, down through the thin ice into the drowning darkness, and saw the darker shapes of gliding carp and trout, and when I looked up again, Gatty was there! She was running round to the other side. Then she, too, bellied onto the ice, and silently began to swim out across it.

Again and again Sian screamed.

Gatty reached her first and grabbed Sian's arm.

'Quiet!' she said fiercely.

When I tried to get hold of Sian's other arm, some of the ice around the hole broke away; then it cracked under me, and I let go of Sian and slid back.

Sian began to scream again.

When I reached out for the second time, I could hear the ice groan and feel it bending.

'Go on!' said Gatty. 'Lift, Sian!'

Sian grabbed Gatty's shoulder, and then my hair. She strained, she moaned, and then all at once she slid out onto her stomach, dripping and mucky and wailing, as if she'd somehow given birth to herself. She'd risen from the darkness into the light, and Gatty and I were the midwives, pulling her up on to the bending ice.

Andrew Brodie: Improving Comprehension for ages 10-11 © A&C Black Publishers Ltd 2008

Broken ice

Name: _____

Date: _____

Answer the questions, using full sentences.

1. From which book does this passage come?

    _____

    _____

2. Who wrote the book?

    _____

3. How old is Arthur? Who has fallen through the ice?

    _____

    _____

4. Who has fallen through the ice?

    _____

    _____

5. What could Arthur see when he looked through the ice?

    _____

    _____

6. The story is told by Arthur. Imagine that you are Sian – tell the story of what happened. Continue on the back of this sheet if you need to.

    _____

    _____

    _____

    _____

    _____

    _____

    _____

    _____

Notes for teachers
Help the children to read this passage, ensuring that they understand the story. Help them to see the story from Sian's point of view. i.e. they could explain how Sian managed to fall through the ice in the first place, how cold the water must have felt and how desperate she must have been to be rescued.

Broken ice

Answer the questions, using full sentences.

1. What is the title of the book from which this passage comes and who wrote it?

    _____

    _____

2. How did Arthur know that Sian was in difficulty?

    _____

    _____

3. What did Sian keep doing?

    _____

    _____

4. What orders did Arthur and Gatty give to Sian?

    _____

    _____

    _____

    _____

    _____

5. What verb is used to describe how Gatty crossed the ice? Why is this a strange use of that verb?

    _____

    _____

    _____

6. The story is told by Arthur. Imagine that you are Gatty. Tell the story of what happened. Include as much description and detail as you can. Write your answer on a separate piece of paper.

Notes for teachers
Read this passage with the children and discuss the main events in the story. Discuss the questions with them. Help them to write their answers by composing the sentences first before they write anything down. Support them in seeing the story from Gatty's point of view. i.e. where was Gatty when Sian fell through the ice and how did Gatty know she was in trouble?

Andrew Brodie: Improving Comprehension for ages 10-11 © A&C Black Publishers Ltd 2008

Broken ice

Name: _____

Date: _____

Answer the questions, using full sentences.

1.   What other books has Kevin Crossley-Holland written? You may need to look on the internet or in a book to find the answer to this question.

   _____

   _____

   _____

2.   What words does the author use to describe the water? Why are these words so effective?

   _____

   _____

   _____

3.   Find all the words that the author has used to describe the ice: its appearance, the noises it makes and the way it feels. Do you think his description is effective?

   _____

   _____

   _____

4.   We can tell from the story that Sian is panicking. How is Gatty reacting to the crisis?

   _____

   _____

5.   What do midwives do? You may need to look in a dictionary to find the answer to this question.

   _____

   _____

6.   On a separate piece of paper imagine that you are involved in a similar rescue. Describe what happens.

Notes for teachers
Help the children to read this passage, ensuring that they understand the story. Discuss the questions with them and support them in writing answers, using correctly punctuated full sentences, by asking them to say their sentences out loud before writing them down. To answer questions 2 and 3 encourage the children to look at the wording very carefully, discussing how the words convey the coldness of the ice, the calmness of Gatty and the danger that all three children faced.

Seasons

Have You Ever?

Have you ever walked down a country lane,
Smelled spring flowers,
Felt soft rain,
Seen birds soar,
Been warmed by the sun,
At the time when spring has just begun?

Have you ever been out picking summer flowers,
In quiet pastures,
Whiling away hours,
Made daisy chains,
And skipped about
Enjoying the days when hot sun is out?

Have you ever watched leaves fall through the air,
Golden brown,
While red poppies flare,
And heading south
Seen geese fly by
And heard their cries in the autumn sky?

Have you ever walked in deep fresh snow,
Crunching footprints
As you go,
Red ears tingle,
Bitter wind cold,
In winter as the year grows old?

Seasons

Spring – new fresh warm green bright alive; full of promise
Summer - long hot days buzzing colourful flowery; the weather peaks
Autumn - mature golden leafy ageing cool blustery; an end approaching
Winter – bare cold silver grey still sleeping stark; closing down

Andrew Brodie: Improving Comprehension for ages 10-11 © A&C Black Publishers Ltd 2008

Seasons

Name: _____

Date: _____

Ring the correct answer for each of the following three questions.

1.   In which season might you make footprints in the snow?

   spring   summer   autumn   winter

2.   In which direction are the geese flying?

   north   south   east   west

3.   How many verses are in each poem?

   two   four   six   eight

Each of the following questions should be answered with a simple sentence. The first one has been started for you.

4.   In the first poem what are the first three words of each verse?

   The first three words of _____

   _____

5.   Which of the two poems does not rhyme?

   _____

   _____

6.   According to the first poem, when would you pick flowers?

   _____

   _____

   _____

7.   On a separate piece of paper draw a picture to show one of the seasons, using the information provided in the poems.

Notes for teachers
Read the poems with the children making sure they have picked up on the rhythm and rhyme in the first one. The final question ask pupils to draw a picture – it is important that this should reflect only the poem and not any other seasonal ideas, i.e. an autumn picture should show geese flying but should not show squirrels preparing to hibernate.

Seasons

Name: _____

Date: _____

1. **Ring the phrase nearest in meaning to 'pastures'.**

    a grassy playground   a tree covered field

    a large garden   an area of grassy land.

2. **Ring the word nearest in meaning to 'blustery'.**

    rainy   sunny   cold   windy

Answer each of the following questions with a sentence.

3. What is the main thing that the two poems have in common?

    _____

    _____

4. Why might ears appear red and what would make them tingle?

    _____

    _____

5. In verse three of 'Seasons' why do you think the word 'ageing' is used.

    _____

    _____

    _____

6. Which of the two poems do you prefer? Give reasons for your answer.

    _____

    _____

    _____

    _____

    _____

Seasons

Name: _____

Date: _____

Answer each of the following questions with well-written detailed sentences.

1. Which of the five senses is not mentioned in either poem? Why do you think this is?

   _____

   _____

   _____

2. Explain the structure of the poem 'Seasons'.

   _____

   _____

   _____

3. Explain the structure of the poem 'Have You Ever?'.

   _____

   _____

   _____

4. Explain the words 'birds soar'.

   _____

   _____

   _____

5. Why might the poet have chosen the word 'flare' when describing the autumn poppies?

   _____

   _____

   _____

6. Following the structure of the poem 'Have you ever' write your own six line poem on a separate piece of paper.

Notes for teachers

When answering the first question pupils should have noticed that taste is not mentioned as there is nothing edible referred to in the poems. When explaining 'birds soar' pupils should show an understanding of the difference between soaring and flying. In explaining 'crunching footprints' pupils should explain that the crunching refers to the sound of feet stepping in snow. The poet chose the word flare to reflect both the brightness and the short period of flowering – both these points should be in an ideal answer.

Andrew Brodie: Improving Comprehension for ages 10-11 © A&C Black Publishers Ltd 2008

From London to Muscat (Part 1)

The journey from London to Muscat is known as a 'long-haul' flight, unlike flights within this country, which are called 'domestic' flights, or flights to destinations in Europe, which are given the term 'short-haul' flights. The title long-haul flight is enough to tell you that you will be sitting in your aeroplane seat for several hours and, unless you are wealthy enough to afford First Class or Business Class, you can expect to be quite uncomfortable.

With these thoughts in mind, the Mackenzie family – Mum, Dad and the twins, Beth and Tom – had packed various items in their hand luggage that could keep themselves busy. Mum had a book of Su Doku puzzles, Dad had the guide-book for Oman, Beth had a book to write in ('you're mad,' Tom had said to her) and Tom had … well, Tom hadn't packed anything. After several arguments, he was the lucky one who had won the right to sit next to the window, as Beth had eventually conceded that actually she didn't care.

Even Mum, who normally feared nothing, looked a little anxious as the plane taxied to its take-off position. "I don't mind once we're up there, but I'm not keen on the take-off," she said.

It seemed ages until the plane reached the runway for take-off but suddenly it began to move forward, then to pick up speed rapidly. Tom felt that he was being pressed into the back of his seat but he was able to turn his head to watch their progress. It certainly was fast. The airport building seemed to be moving very quickly in the opposite direction to Tom and then, the moment he had been waiting for, the plane made a shallow angle with the ground and they were airborne. The houses and cars and a river and a reservoir and a railway line and some fields with cows in looked so strange from above.

Tom felt absolutely exhilarated and he glanced around to see if the others were excited as him. He couldn't believe what he saw! Mum had her eyes closed, Dad was reading the papers and Beth was already writing.

He turned to look through the window again. He couldn't see a thing – just

whiteness – but then the plane shot out of the cloud and into bright sunshine and the world, as far as Tom could see, consisted of an endless bumpy, rolling 'landscape' of brightly lit white clouds, which were below him rather than above him. In the distance a spark of light caught his attention then he realised that the sun had reflected off another plane and he watched that plane's progress until his own plane's engines changed tone and it levelled out after the climb.

Andrew Brodie: Improving Comprehension for ages 10-11 © A&C Black Publishers Ltd 2008

From London to Muscat (Part 1)

Name: _____

Date: _____

Answer the questions, using full sentences.

1. What is a long-haul flight?

   _____

   _____

   _____

2. What is a domestic flight?

   _____

   _____

   _____

3. What is the name of the family who are travelling?

   _____

   _____

4. What is their destination?

   _____

   _____

5. Which member of the family had not prepared anything to do on the flight?

   _____

   _____

6. List all of the things Tom saw when he looked out of the window.

   _____   _____

   _____   _____

   _____   _____

   _____   _____

Notes for teachers
Read this passage together and ensure the children understand the main events. Encourage the children to notice the structure of the text particularly how the first paragraph provides background information before the family is introduced. When considering the last question encourage the children to reread the whole passage, perhaps underlining or highlighting the things that Tom saw.

From London to Muscat (Part 1)

Name: _____

Date: _____

Answer the questions, using full sentences.

1. To which city are the family travelling?

   _____

   _____

2. In what country is that city? How do you know this?

   _____

   _____

   _____

3. Why did Beth let Tom sit next to the window?

   _____

   _____

4. Why did Tom think Beth was mad?

   _____

   _____

5. Why was Tom surprised when he looked round at the other members of his family?

   _____

   _____

   _____

6. Find London and Muscat on a map and look at the shortest route between them. Make a list of the countries that you think the flight might cross over.

   _____   _____

   _____   _____

   _____   _____

Notes for teachers

Help the children to read this passage and ensure that they understand the story. Discuss the questions with them and encourage them to compose their answers out loud before writing anything down. Some of the questions require the children to 'read between the lines' and to find evidence for their interpretations. Help them to find an appropriate map or atlas to use for question 6.

Andrew Brodie: Improving Comprehension for ages 10-11 © A&C Black Publishers Ltd 2008

From London to Muscat (Part 1)

Name: _____

Date: _____

Answer the questions, using full sentences.

1. Give an example of a short-haul flight, a domestic flight and a long-haul flight.

   _____

   _____

   _____

   _____

2. In which parts of the plane could you be most comfortable?

   _____

   _____

3. What is 'hand luggage'?

   _____

   _____

4. What was Mum worried about?

   _____

   _____

5. Why, at one point, could Tom only see whiteness?

   _____

   _____

6. In what part of the world is Oman?

   _____

   _____

7. List the names of at least five other countries that are in that area.

   _____   _____

   _____   _____

   _____   _____

Notes for teachers
Help the children to read this passage and ensure that they understand the story. Can they remember the main events? Discuss the questions with them and encourage them to compose their answers out loud before writing anything down. Some of the questions require the children to 'read between the lines' and to find evidence for their interpretations. Help them to find an appropriate map or atlas and in deciding which countries may be on the route.

Andrew Brodie: Improving Comprehension for ages 10-11 © A&C Black Publishers Ltd 2008

From London to Muscat (Part 2)

Tom had discovered that his seat area featured a range of gadgets for his entertainment. There was a button to press to make the seat recline should you want to go to sleep, which he didn't. Still, he tried it out several times until the person in the seat behind said, "Do you mind?" in quite a cross voice.

"No!" Tom had replied, then his mum had said, "Tom!" to him, in an even crosser voice, and, "Very sorry," in a smiley sort of voice, to the person behind.

So Tom tried everything else. There was an elasticated net fastened to the back of the seat in front, designed to hold the airline company's in-flight magazine plus their catalogue showing items that could be bought on the plane and some sick bags.

"What are these for?" Tom asked his mum.

"They're for people to be sick in if they get travel sickness," she replied.

Tom had been feeling fine, but, now his mum had come to mention it, perhaps he was feeling a little queasy. He grabbed one of the bags, opened its mouth wide and made what he hoped were throwing up noises into it.

"Tom!" said his dad in an even crosser voice than his mum had used. Beth just looked up from her writing, rolled her eyes, and started writing again.

Tom sat back. What could he do now?

In the head-rest of the seat in front there was a small screen and in the arm-rest of his own seat was a device that looked a bit like a remote control only Tom thought it wasn't 'remote' because when you pulled it out of the arm-rest you found that it was connected to it by a long, thin, retractable wire. However, it worked in much the same way and, when he pressed the correct button, the screen flashed into life.

Tom found that there were dozens of channels available so he started to check each one. Film, film, film, cartoon, film starting, film ending, cartoon, film, news, news in Arabic, old television programme, film, another old television programme, map.

Tom looked carefully at the map. This was interesting …

Andrew Brodie: Improving Comprehension for ages 10-11 © A&C Black Publishers Ltd 2008

From London to Muscat (Part 2)

Name: _____

Date: _____

Answer the questions, using full sentences.

1. What did the button on Tom's seat do?

    _____

    _____

2. What was the elasticated net for?

    _____

    _____

3. Why did Dad get cross with Tom?

    _____

    _____

4. What did Tom discover in the head-rest of the seat in front of him?

    _____

    _____

5. How did Tom switch the screen on?

    _____

    _____

6. Make a list of the programmes Tom found, by counting each type of
    programme e.g. Tom found two cartoons.

    _____

    _____

    _____

    _____

    _____

    _____

    _____

    _____

Notes for teachers
Help the children to read this passage and discuss the main events of the story. Some of the vocabulary is difficult and will require the children to infer meanings using syntax and context. When considering the last question, encourage the children to count each type of programme carefully.

Andrew Brodie: Improving Comprehension for ages 10-11 © A&C Black Publishers Ltd 2008

From London to Muscat (Part 2)

Answer the questions, using full sentences.

1. Why did the person in the seat behind Tom say, 'do you mind?'?

   _____

   _____

2. Did Tom give a polite reply?

   _____

   _____

3. Why did Beth roll her eyes?

   _____

   _____

4. What does 'retractable' mean? You may need to look this word up in a dictionary but you should try to use your own words to explain it.

   _____

   _____

   _____

5. Why was one of the news channels in Arabic?

   _____

   _____

6. Make a list of the all the things that Tom did to amuse himself. Which of these things would be annoying to other people?

   _____

   _____

   _____

   _____

Notes for teachers

Help the children to read this passage and ensure that they understand the main event of the story. Can they appreciate the points of view of Tom, the passenge behind Tom and Tom's mum? When considering the last question, encourage the children to reread the passage, underlining or highlighting the relevant sentences.

From London to Muscat (Part 2)

Name: _____

Date: _____

Answer the questions, using full sentences.

1. Why was Tom trying things out?

   _____

   _____

2. In your own words describe how Mum spoke to the person sitting behind Tom.

   _____

   _____

   _____

3. Use a dictionary to find the definitions of 'remote' and 'remote control'.

   _____

   _____

   _____

   _____

4. Was Tom correct in thinking that the device was not actually a 'remote control' device?

   _____

   _____

   _____

5. What sort of boy do you think Tom is? Try to describe him.

   _____

   _____

   _____

   _____

   _____

Notes for teachers
Help the children to read this passage and ensure that they understand the story. When considering the last question, encourage the children to think about all the electronic devices that they may have at home but also other 'toys'. Encourage the children to infer the meaning of the word 'gadget' from the text, then to look it up in a dictionary. Discuss with the children which 'gadget' that are designed for entertainment they have at home.

Andrew Brodie: Improving Comprehension for ages 10-11 © A&C Black Publishers Ltd 2008

From London to Muscat (Part 3)

Tom stared at the map on the screen in the back of the head-rest of the seat in front. It showed a map of Europe and part of Asia and it had a long dotted line that stretched from London to Abu Dhabi and a short dotted line that connected Abu Dhabi to Muscat. The names of the three cities were marked on the map. About halfway along the longer line there was a flashing picture of an aeroplane, clearly headed away from London.

Suddenly the map changed to a closer view and other cities' names appeared: Sofia, Istanbul, Bucharest, Athens, Ankara, Aleppo. Then the map disappeared and information appeared in its place:

Distance from London 2972km

Distance to Abu Dhabi 2496km

Time in London 16:25

Time in Abu Dhabi 20:25

Time of arrival in Abu Dhabi 23:49 local time

Tom did some calculations: It would be three hours and twenty-four minutes until they arrived in Abu Dhabi so that was about three and a half hours. Dad told him that they would be there for about half an hour so that was about four hours until they took off from Abu Dhabi. The flight to Muscat from Abu Dhabi

would take about three quarters of an hour so there was about four and three quarter hours to go until they finally arrived.

Tom couldn't wait. He was really looking forward to the landing and take-off in Abu Dhabi and the landing in Muscat, especially as he would get such a good view of the lights because he had the window seat. He wondered what to do next. Watch a film? Annoy Beth? Watch a film? Annoy Beth?

He turned to look at Beth. She had been writing for most of the journey so far, but now she had headphones on and was staring at the screen in front of her. Tom noticed that her 'remote control' was still fastened to the arm-rest of her seat. He reached out and pressed the number 7 on her remote then pulled his hand back slowly and gazed straight ahead.

Beth sat bolt upright as though she had been stung by a wasp.

"What is it love?" asked Mum. "What's the matter?"

"My screen changed channel. I didn't touch it or anything."

"That sounds fishy!" said Mum, looking round at Tom's smirking face. "Ok, Tom, I think it's Beth's turn by the window now. Swap over. In fact, Beth can go by the window and you can swap with me. I'll sit by Beth and you can sit in the middle seats with Dad."

Andrew Brodie: Improving Comprehension for ages 10-11 © A&C Black Publishers Ltd 2008

From London to Muscat (Part 3)

Name: _____

Date: _____

Answer the questions, except for the third one, using full sentences.

1. To which city did the first dotted line connect London?

   _____

   _____

2. What could Tom see halfway along the first dotted line?

   _____

   _____

3. Altogether Tom has seen the names of four cities beginning with A. Write these cities in alphabetical order.

   _____

   _____

   _____

   _____

4. What was Tom most looking forward to?

   _____

   _____

   _____

5. Why did Beth sit bolt upright?

   _____

   _____

   _____

6. Imagine that you are Tom. On separate piece of paper describe how you feel about having to move seats.

Notes for teachers

Help the children to read this passage and ensure that they understand the story. When considering the last question encourage the children to try to think like Tom: Who would you be cross with? What feelings would you have inside you? Do you think it's right that you have been made to move? This process will help the pupils understand the themes, causes and points of view within the text.

Andrew Brodie: Improving Comprehension for ages 10-11 © A&C Black Publishers Ltd 2008

From London to Muscat (Part 3)

Name: _____

Date: _____

Answer the questions, using full sentences.

1. Why did the information show the distance to Abu Dhabi instead of Muscat?

   _____

   _____

   _____

2. How many hours ahead was Abu Dhabi?

   _____

   _____

3. What was Tom expecting to get a good view of?

   _____

   _____

4. What two choices did Tom feel that he had to keep himself amused?

   _____

   _____

   _____

5. How did Tom try to conceal the fact that he had changed the channel on Beth's screen and how did Mum know that he had done so?

   _____

   _____

   _____

   _____

6. What do you think happens next? Write a short description on a separate piece of paper.

Notes for teachers
Some children may need help with the mathematical aspects of the time conversions. Encourage them to use words and language in their own writing that reflect the scenes, causes and points of view contained in the story.

Andrew Brodie: Improving Comprehension for ages 10-11 © A&C Black Publishers Ltd 2008

From London to Muscat (Part 3)

Name: _____

Date: _____

Answer the questions, except for the first one, using full sentences.

1. Using a map, atlas or the internet find out in which country each of the six cities, mentioned in paragraph two, is situated.

    _____   _____

    _____   _____

    _____   _____

2. Is the aeroplane more than or less than halfway between London and Abu Dhabi? Explain your answer.

    _____

    _____

    _____

3. At what time can Tom expect to arrive in Muscat?

    _____

    _____

4. Why has the writer written 'remote control' in inverted commas? You may need to look back at London to Muscat (Part 2) to help you with this answer.

    _____

    _____

    _____

5. How close to the window does Tom end up?

    _____

    _____

    _____

6. On a separate piece of paper imagine that you are one of the other members of the Mackenzie family. Describe your journey so far.

Andrew Brodie: Improving Comprehension for ages 10-11 © A&C Black Publishers Ltd 2008

The Midnight Fox

The text below is an extract from 'The Midnight Fox' by Betsy Byars. The story is set in North America, where the central character, Tom, is staying on a farm for the summer with his aunt and uncle. It is here that he sees a black fox and is afraid that it might be killed because of the danger it could pose to the poultry on his uncle's farm.

The days and weeks passed quickly, long warm days in which I walked through the woods looking for the black fox.

The next time I saw her was in the late afternoon at the ravine.

This was my favourite place in the forest. The sides of the ravine were heavy dark boulders with mosses and ferns growing between the rocks, and at the bottom were trunks of old dead trees. The trunks were like statues in some old jungle temple, idols that had fallen and broken and would soon be lost in the creeping foliage. There was only an occasional patch of sunlight.

At the top of the ravine was a flat ledge that stuck out over the rocks, and I was lying there on my stomach this particular afternoon. The rock was warm because the sun had been on it since noon and I was half asleep when suddenly I saw something move below me. It was the black fox. There was a certain lightness, a quickness that I could not miss.

She came over the rocks as easily as a cat. Her tail was very high and full, like a sail that was bearing her forward. Her fur was black as coal, and when she was in the shadows all I could see was the white tip of her tail.

As I watched, she moved with great ease over one of the fallen trees, ran up the other side of the ravine, and disappeared into the underbrush.

I stayed exactly where I was. My head was resting on my arms, and everything was so still I could hear the ticking of my watch. I wanted to sit up. I am sort of a bony person and after I have been lying on something hard for a long time, I get very uncomfortable. This afternoon, however, I did not move; I had the feeling that the fox was going to come back through the ravine and I did not want to miss seeing her.

Andrew Brodie: Improving Comprehension for ages 10-11 © A&C Black Publishers Ltd 2008

The Midnight Fox

Name: _____

Date: _____

Ring the correct answer for each of the following three questions.

1. What is the title of the book from which the extract was taken?

    The midday   The midnight   The midday   The midnight
       fox   wolf   wolf   fox

2. What time of the year does the story take place?

    Spring   Summer   Autumn   Winter

3. What colour is the fox in the story?

    brown   black   white   navy

Each of the following questions should be answered with a simple sentence. The first one has been started for you.

4. What is the name of the central character in the story?

    The central character _____

5. What was the character doing on the afternoon of the story?

    _____

    _____

6. What colour was the tip of the fox's tail?

    _____

    _____

7. After the fox had disappeared into the underbrush, why didn't Tom move?

    _____

    _____

    _____

    _____

Notes for teachers

Ensure the children have read and understood the passage, paying particular attention to any unfamiliar vocabulary. Encourage pupils to write their sentences correctly when completing the second group of questions. Pay particular attention to the use of capital letters and full stops. All the words pupils need to use are in the questions or the text so it is important to encourage pupils to use correct spellings when writing their answers.

58

The Midnight Fox

Name: _____

Date: _____

Answer each of the following questions with a sentence.

1. In which continent is the story set?

    _____

    _____

2. Why do you think the story is called 'The Midnight Fox'?

    _____

    _____

    _____

3. Tom was on a flat rock. Why was the rock warm?

    _____

    _____

4. How were the old dead tree trunks described in the text?

    _____

    _____

    _____

    _____

5. Which words in the text tell you that it was shady at the bottom of the ravine?

    _____

    _____

    _____

6. Imagine you were the writer waiting for the fox to come back. On a separate piece of paper write the next part of the story. Jot down some ideas on the lines below.

    _____

    _____

    _____

Notes for teachers
For the final task, the pupils should consider these ideas. How long do you wait? How uncomfortable are you?
Does the fox return? if so, how close does she get to you?

Andrew Brodie: Improving Comprehension for ages 10-11 © A&C Black Publishers Ltd 2008

The Midnight Fox

Name: _____

Date: _____

Answer each of the following questions with a well-written detailed sentence.

1. Why did Tom go walking in the woods most days?

    _____

    _____

    _____

2. What first alerted Tom to the presence of the fox?

    _____

    _____

    _____

3. Why is Tom afraid that the black fox could be killed?

    _____

    _____

    _____

4. Why, in the future, would the dead tree trunks not be seen at the bottom of the ravine?

    _____

    _____

    _____

5. Why was Tom described as being half asleep before he saw the fox?

    _____

    _____

6. On the lines below write a definition of the word 'ravine'.

    ravine _____

    _____

Notes for teachers

The final question asks for a definition. This should initially be done without reference to a dictionary. You may later wish to discuss the pupils' ideas of what a ravine is. Can the children infer the meaning from the text? Compare their ideas with a dictionary definition. NB – a correct definition should include the words deep, narrow and valley.

Andrew Brodie: Improving Comprehension for ages 10-11 © A&C Black Publishers Ltd 2008

End of term

The text below is from 'The Turbulent Term of Tyke Tiler' by Gene Kemp. The extract is taken from towards the end of the book where the children in the story are about to leave their school.

We emptied our desks and took the pictures off the wall. Miss came back for the end of term concert, where we stood up and the school clapped and cheered us. The back of our classroom was full of costumes and scenery heaped into boxes. We didn't think about it being the end of term. We thought about the play. Patsy and Miss and me, we sat behind the curtains and the others got ready to go on the stage while we told the story of the quests, of the legend of the Grail and of Lancelot and Guinevere.

Danny was fantastic as Galahad. Everyone was fantastic and the school stood up and clapped and cheered us. The Headmaster said a prayer for the school and a special one for those leaving. Then we sang, 'Lord Dismiss Us With Thy Blessing' while Linda and Lorraine sobbed and wailed in the back row.

We cheered the Staff and the Headmaster, and then the school. That cheer nearly lifted the roof off.

And it was over.

We went to get our shoebags out of the cloakroom.

'Good-bye. Good-bye.'

'See you.'

Danny and Pithead had disappeared so I wandered into the playground to wait for them. Already the school was emptying. Tonight we would go down to the river and count all the weeks of glorious summer ahead of us. All the long days of nothing to do. Summer holiday days. I stared at the old building and the tall tree in the playground. It was the last time I should be here. No more Sir, gloom. No more Mrs Somers, FANTASTIC. I'd come here, holding Berry's hand, when I was four, and now I was twelve. Eight years had gone somewhere. And I didn't want to go to a new school. And I didn't want to grow up. Growing up seemed a grotty sort of thing to have to do. I felt empty, strange, restless.

I looked up at the bell tower. The bell tower I'd never climbed. There it was, unrung since the war. What a waste. What a pity it was never rung. A bell like that was meant to be rung. It winked at me in the sunlight, full of invitation. What an end to eight years. I could guess where Thomas Tiler had climbed up, ages ago. There was an easy route. Perfectly simple. Simply perfect. I walked up to the wall and walked away again.

Andrew Brodie: Improving Comprehension for ages 10-11 © A&C Black Publishers Ltd 2008

Name: _____

Date: _____

Ring the correct answer for each of the following three questions.

1. Who was Galahad in the end of term play?

    Tyke   Danny   Thomas   Pithead

2. What time of the year was it?

    spring   summer   autumn   winter.

3. What was in the bell tower?

    a bell   a wall   Thomas Tiler   nothing

Each of the following questions should be answered with a simple sentence. The first one has been started for you.

4. What did the children get out of the cloakroom?

    The children got _____

5. What hymn did they sing before school closed?

    _____

    _____

6. What was heaped into boxes at the back of the classroom?

    _____

    _____

7. What was the title of the story that the text is from?

    _____

    _____

Notes for teachers

Ensure the children have read and understood the passage, paying particular attention to any unfamiliar vocabulary. Discuss the first three questions with them, encouraging them to explain how they know the correct answers – they should be able to find supporting evidence from the text. All the words pupils need to use are in the questions or the text so it is important to encourage pupils to use correct spellings when writing their answers.

62

Name: _____

Date: _____

Answer each of the following questions with a sentence.

1. Name the two children sitting behind the curtain with 'Miss'.

   _____

   _____

2. Write the sentence in the text that tells us that the children were about to leave the school.

   _____

   _____

   _____

3. What was Tyke planning to do that evening?

   _____

   _____

4. Where did Tyke wait for Danny and Pithead?

   _____

   _____

5. How long had Tyke been going to the school?

   _____

   _____

6. Explain what is meant in the last paragraph by, 'It winked at me in the sunlight'.

   _____

   _____

7. What are you going to do on the last day of the school year? Write your answer on a separate piece of paper.

Notes for teachers

Ensure the children have read and understood the passage, paying particular attention to any unfamiliar vocabulary. The questions on this page ask pupils to use complete sentences; these should be correctly spelled and punctuated. Encourage the children to read the questions carefully and incorporate some evidence into their answers.

Andrew Brodie: Improving Comprehension for ages 10-11 © A&C Black Publishers Ltd 2008

End of term

Name: _____

Date: _____

Answer each of the following questions with a well-written detailed sentence.

1. Explain why Linda and Lorraine 'sobbed and wailed' at the school concert.

   _____

   _____

2. Explain what is meant by 'That cheer nearly lifted the roof off'.

   _____

   _____

4. In the text why is the word FANTASTIC printed in capital letters?

   _____

   _____

5. What reason does Tyke give for not wanting to grow up?

   _____

   _____

6. Explain what Tyke is thinking of doing in the last paragraph and why you think this.

   _____

   _____

   _____

   _____

7. Write a definition for the word 'legend'.

   Legend _____

   _____

8. Write a definition for the word 'quest'.

   Quest _____

   _____

Notes for teachers

The first five questions need full sentences as answers. These should be detailed and correctly punctuated and spelled and should include evidence from the text. The final two questions ask for definitions. Pupils should not use dictionaries to do these, though you may wish to refer to a dictionary later when discussing the ideas that pupils have offered.